Where Golfers Buy Their Pants

M000284478

Where Golfers Buy Their Pants
And Other Collected Cartoons

Sports Cartoons by
STEVE MOORE

MACMILLAN • USA

Copyright © 1994 by Tribune Media Services, Inc.

This is a work of fiction. Names, characters, places, and incidents either are the product of the author's imagination or are used fictitiously. Any resemblance to actual events or persons, living or dead, is entirely coincidental.

All rights reserved. No part of this book may be reproduced or transmitted in any form or by any means, electronic or mechanical, including photocopying, recording, or by any information storage and retrieval system, without permission in writing from the Publisher.

Macmillan Publishing Company
15 Columbus Circle
New York, NY 10023

MACMILLAN is a registered trademark of Macmillan, Inc.

           Library of Congress Cataloging-in-Publication Data
Moore, Steve.
   Where golfers buy their pants and other collected cartoons /
   Steve Moore. — 1st ed.
       p.   cm.
   ISBN 0-02-035127-5
   1. Golf—Caricatures and cartoons.   2. American wit and
   humor, Pictorial.   I. Title.
   NC1429.M727A4   1994
   741.5'973—dc20   94-593   CIP

10   9   8   7   6   5   4   3   2   1

Printed in the United States of America

To my mom

©1991 Tribune Media Services, Inc.
All Rights Reserved

"Whoa, whoa, whoa! What, are you crazy, Leonard? You'll get cramps. Wait 20 minutes to digest before you go in the water."

©1991 Tribune Media Services, Inc.
All Rights Reserved

"Well, we're doomed. They didn't see us, and that was our last flare."

© 1991 Tribune Media Services, Inc.
All Rights Reserved

"Back off, Fred, you heard him wrong. He said you have a really big putt."

© 1991 Tribune Media Services, Inc.
All Rights Reserved

"Surrounded by munchkins on the first tee, attacked by flying monkeys on the seventh, now this ... I say we skip the back nine, Herb."

© 1991 Tribune Media Services, Inc.
All Rights Reserved

© 1991 Tribune Media Services, Inc.
All Rights Reserved

"How many times did I warn you, Frank? How many times? I said stay away from the roughs, Frank."

10

"Crud! Wouldn't you know it. Right into a land
hazard ..."

"I need a new golf cart ... And you might want to send a doctor out to the 9th green."

©1986 Tribune Media Services, Inc.
All Rights Reserved

3-7

"Bob, you run back to the clubhouse and call their wives. I'll try to find us another twosome."

...FORMER PRESIDENT FORD TEES OFF AND...WHOA!!

©1986 Tribune Media Services, Inc.
All Rights Reserved

4-26

© 1989 Tribune Media Services, Inc.
All Rights Reserved

"I said hand me the *putter*."

© 1988 Tribune Media Services, Inc.
All Rights Reserved

18TH HOLE

3,755 MILES
7 STATES; PAR 5

14

Dr. Feldman's fall from grace was swift and he was inevitably branded a heretic and shunned by his peers in the medical community.

"Ha! Right smack in the middle of a grass trap!!"

The deadly Venus Golfer Trap

©1988 Tribune Media Services, Inc.
All Rights Reserved

"Excuse me, Mr. Oliver, but there are two gentlemen here who would like to play through..."

©1989 Tribune Media Services, Inc.
All Rights Reserved

" ... Aah, aah *SHANK IT!* ... Whoa, excuse me ... *SHANK IT!* ... hoo, must be an allergy ... aah, aah, aaaah *SHANK IT!!* ... sorry ... "

©1988 Tribune Media Services, Inc.
All Rights Reserved

"OK, I think I understand: Head down. Slow backswing. Then just barely knick the ball so it only travels about five feet."

©1992 Tribune Media Services, Inc.
All Rights Reserved

18

"It's working ... "

"Goodbye, dear. Have a good game."

" ... OK, OK, Bob. I promise to keep quiet while you're trying to putt ... Bob? Joke's over, Bob ... Bob??"

© 1991 Tribune Media Services, Inc.
All Rights Reserved

"Hey, Bob ... what does this word mean: 'Skeletonize'?"

© 1991 Tribune Media Services, Inc.
All Rights Reserved

Synchronized golfing

©1989 Tribune Media Services, Inc.
All Rights Reserved

BALL WASH

PLUNGE

BOOM!!!

BALL WASH

11-30

©1989 Tribune Media Services, Inc.
All Rights Reserved

8-5

" ... Well, I guess it was about, oh, a hundred-
yard shot over a sand trap, and ... Hey Earl!
Did I nail him with a seven or eight iron?"

©1989 Tribune Media Services, Inc.
All Rights Reserved

"You've got 'golfer's toe' and, if I'm not mistaken, early symptoms of 'golf on the brain' ... "

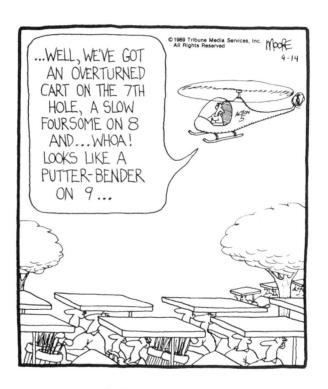

©1989 Tribune Media Services, Inc.
All Rights Reserved

Golf course gridlock

25

Every spring the golfers are flushed from the fairways and into nets where they are tagged and released relatively unharmed.

© 1988 Tribune Media Services, Inc.
All Rights Reserved

"Keep it up, Floyd ...scream and yell ... we'll see how you like it when you're trying to concentrate ... "

© 1986 Tribune Media Services, Inc.
All Rights Reserved

CLUBHOUSE

Where golfers buy their pants.

"Now, I'll ask you again ... mind if we play through?"

" ... So then Larry hits his tee shot, and the ball ... Dang! Larry, I forget, is it a 'hook' or a 'slice' when the ball sails off to the right?"

" ... Wait, here it is. 'The other members of the foursome may either dislodge the player or take a penalty stroke and continue without him' ..."

"Yo!! Mind if we play through?"

"I think you'd better drive the cart."

"Look, don't worry about it, Bob. I mean, if they live in a house next to a fairway they've got to expect occasional damage from errant golf balls ..."

"Four!!"

Pinocchio takes up golf

"Wow. Poor Dewey. Engulfed in a celestial vortex and sucked from the face of the Earth ... dibs on his clubs!"

35

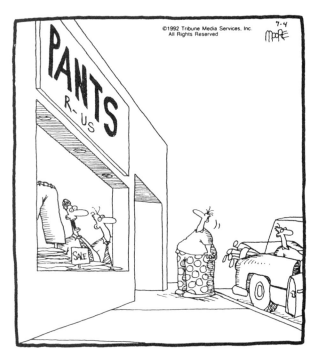

"Golfers! Quick, hide the tasteful stuff!!"

"Hop out. Your ball landed right about here."

"I hate the first tee. I always feel so self-conscious,
like my every move is being watched."

"Yo! ... Need a fourth?"

"Hop on. They were out of carts."

The Putter of Excalibur

"... A great guy, a loving husband and, uh, we're-really-going-to-miss-him-amen ... OK, let's putt out. The foursome behind us is waiting to tee off."

PGA officials later reversed themselves and rescinded the decision to allow heckling at tournaments.

"Look, Bob, maybe you should just play another ball."

© 1990 Tribune Media Services, Inc.
All Rights Reserved

KEEP
GOLF CARTS
ON PATH
AT ALL TIMES

8-8

© 1990 Tribune Media Services, Inc.
All Rights Reserved

8-2

"Never fails ... always just as I'm about to putt."

"There's my ball. Stay in the cart, Floyd."

"Hurry. She's starting to come to."

"Thank God! Kenny! Someone's spotted us!!"

Sister Mary Francis salvages a par.

"Well shoot, Ted. Here's why you're not getting any distance... You're suppose to take that little sock thingy off the head of your club."

49

" ... OK, OK, OK, OK!! You can play through!!!"

"You must have sunk it. Dewey's screaming."

"You think we should report this to the pro shop?"

"Listen carefully, Don. Run to the clubhouse, explain what happened to Bob and get back here pronto. There's a foursome behind us waiting to tee off."

Golf defined

Stationary golf cart: All the aerobic benfits of riding around for 18 holes, but in the privacy of your home or office!

"Whoa, that's a nasty hook you've got there, Doug. Try moving farther back in the seat and straighten your left elbow."

Getting in shape with golf

Step aerobics for golfers

55

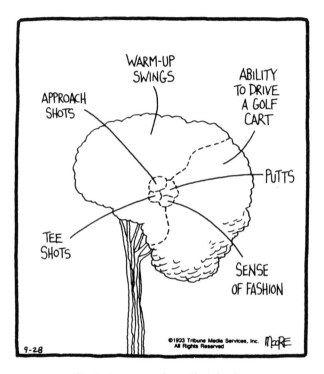

Control centers of a golfer's brain

"Wait! He didn't win, majesty. I added wrong. You actually won by a stroke."

©1993 Tribune Media Services, Inc.
All Rights Reserved

"We found the groaning noise, Mrs. Lieberman. Your husband was lodged under the axle."

©1993 Tribune Media Services, Inc.
All Rights Reserved

"Uh, uh, uh ... you're coming dangerously close to being audible, Mr. Koss. Whisper, Mr. Koss. This isn't a hockey game."

"Gosh, dad, Richy and I were just tearing apart a golf ball to see what was inside ..."

"I'm serious, Wayne. I really think that, just this once, you should go back and replace your divot."

©1993 Tribune Media Services, Inc.
All Rights Reserved

"Take cover ..."

"Go ahead and putt. He just said his ball
rolled over the edge of the yeeeaaaah ..."

"I did it, I did it! A once-in-a-lifetime hole in one! And thank goodness you're here as a witness, Bob!!"

Fall from Eden: the untold story

"The heck with it. You want to go play some tennis?"

"OK, now this next hole goes straight for about 100 yards, then angles off in the shape of a you-know-what leg ..."

© 1988 Tribune Media Services, Inc.
All Rights Reserved

"Beautiful drive, Bob ... You were supposed to tee off in the other direction, though ...

© 1988 Tribune Media Services, Inc.
All Rights Reserved

"Joe, you fool, replace your divot!"

"I think he's trying to tell us something. Yo, Bob! If you've thrown your back out, blink three times!"

"I don't like the foursome you put me with."

67

Roy eventually found his ball, but soon realized that perhaps he had wandered too far into the rough.

©1987 Tribune Media Services, Inc.
All Rights Reserved

"Did you see where it landed, Roy?"

©1987 Tribune Media Services, Inc.
All Rights Reserved

"... But wait, Bob, here's some good news. According to this, you'll only be assessed a one-stroke penalty."

"You've got to ease up on your backswing, Roy."

Life 101

Wolves in the rough

"Well, it's definitely some kind of creature, but I'd say it's only about twice the size of a golf cart."

72

Hustler preying upon the fashion-impaired.

Golf balls for brains

Futile attempts

"You're right, Dick, it does look like Armageddan ... WAAAH! Did you see that?! I sank a chip shot! I sank a chip shot!!"

"Don't be a fool, Andy. Let them play through."

The truth about water hazards

"That was pretty good ... you kept your eyes
on the ball. Head down. Nice follow-through
... now let's work on your grip."

©1993 Tribune Media Services, Inc. All Rights Reserved

"It'll probably break toward the water."

©1992 Tribune Media Services, Inc. All Rights Reserved

"Whoa, whoa, whoa! What are you forgetting, Larry? I can't believe you were going to just walk away without replacing your divot."

Funeral for a golfer

''Whoa, bummer. Close, but no cigar. You don't get in ... next!!''

Further evidence that God is into golf

"Keep it up, Ethel. You can make deep, threatening guttural sounds until you're blue in the face. I'm not going to let it ruin my game."

Robert was not very good, but loved the excercise and opportunity to network.

"Oh, no you don't, Floyd! March right back in here and replace your divot!!"

"We ventured off the designated cart path."

"Now don't panic ... I'll go phone his wife. You stay here and figure out why your shots keep veering off so sharply ... "

Assorted hooligans

Arnold Palmer as a kid

"Bummer about your back, Andy. Don't move. Paramedics will be here soon. Meanwhile, let's say – God forbid – your back is history. No more golf. I'm just talking worst case, OK? ... Can I have your clubs, Andy?"

"Just swat it away, Alice. This is a golf course. There's bound to be insects."

The tournament is posponed as golfballs the size of hail begin to fall.

Miracle of the hooks and slices

Cypress Sholes Country Club and Crocodile Reserve